Presented to Cameron Dale
Dec. 25, 1948

by Primary Dept. Congregational
Sunday School.

Standard Bible Story Readers

BOOK TWO

BY

LILLIE A. FARIS

Former First Grade Critic Teacher, College of Education
of Ohio University, Athens, O.

THE STANDARD PUBLISHING COMPANY

CINCINNATI, O.

First Edition by Lillie A. Faris.
Second Edition Edited by Dorothy Fay Foster.

GRATEFUL ACKNOWLEDGMENT
Is made to the hundreds of friends whose sympathetic
encouragement made possible the publication
of
Standard Bible Story Readers.

CONTENTS

6

A SWEET PROMISE

Laddie, I will walk with you,
  If roads are dark or fair;
Only place your hand in mine,
  And I will guide you there.

Trust me, for I will not fail;
  I will help you day by day;
I will always guard and keep you
  At home, at school, at play.

THE PLANTING

Into the earth, little seed,
    You must go,
Else you will never grow up,
    Don't you know?
I'll tuck you in snugly;
    The sun and the rain
Will help you to come
    Through the ground once again.

Cuddle down, little seed,
    In your cosy bed;
I'll watch for the day
    When you lift up your head.
The birdies will sing
    A sweet lullaby,
While under the ground
    You quietly lie.

When you wake, little seed,
　And creep to the light,
You will hear the tap, tap,
　Of the raindrops bright;
You will see the sun-fairies
　Playing about,
And coaxing the rest
　Of your family out.

Down in your heart, little seed,
　Don't you know,
God put a wee germ,
　To help you to grow?
So hurry, dear seed,
　And come up right away;
I'll be there to watch,
　And to love you each day.

11

THE BIRDS' NEST

High in the treetop's leafy bough
The birdies are building a nest:
'Twas God the Father taught them how
To build every birdie his best.

This is the little birdies' nest
They build in the treetop so high;
And while they cuddle down to rest,
The leaves sing their lullaby.

This is the mother-bird that brings
   The wee little birdies their food;
And this is the father-bird that sings
   And watches all day o'er his brood.

These are the little birds we love,
   That live in the treetop so high;
And He who rules the world above
   Looks down on each one from the sky.

—B. B. Selby.

13

WHAT THE BEE SAID

Busy bee, in your little house
    Among the pretty flowers,
What do you, pray? and what do you say,
    Through all the sunny hours?

"I fly about, and in and out
    Of the little house I go;
      I'm always at work;
      For I never shirk.
    I am very busy, you know.

"I sing a song as I'm working;
    'Buzz buzz!' the livelong day.
      You may think it's funny,
      To sing, gathering honey,
    But to me it's a very fine way."

"Work, while you hum and sing;
   Your day it will brighten,
   Your task it will lighten,
And gladness to you it will bring."

THE GIFT OF WATER

"He sendeth forth springs
    into the valleys;
They run among the mountains;
They give drink to every beast
    of the field.
By them the birds of the heavens
    have their habitation;
They sing among the branches.
He watereth the mountains
    from his chambers;
The earth is filled with the fruit
    of thy works.
He causeth the grass to grow
    for the cattle,
And herb for the service of man;
That he may bring forth food
    out of the earth."

—Ps. 104: 10-14.

16

 A20

THE NEW COAT

One day a little boy's mother went to
the store and bought him a coat.
The boy was pleased, and when he tried
it on, it was just right.
He said, "Oh, thank you, mother, thank
you for my nice new coat."

The mother said, "Don't thank me; thank the storekeeper."

The little boy went down to the store. He said, "I came to thank you for my new coat."

The storekeeper said, "Don't thank me; thank the tailor who made the coat."

The little boy ran to the tailor.

   He said, "Thank you, tailor; thank
   you for my nice new coat."

The tailor said, "Don't thank me; I only
   made the coat. Thank the weaver
   who made the cloth."

Then the boy went to the woolen mills.

He saw all the people making cloth.
He saw one man who was not weaving.
He went up to the man and said, "Oh,
thank you, sir; thank you for my
nice new coat."
The man said, "Don't thank me; thank
the farmer who brought the wool."

21

The little boy ran to the farmer.

He said, "Oh, thank you, farmer; thank
you for my nice new coat."

The farmer said, "Don't thank me; my
sheep gave the wool to me. Go to
the pasture and thank my sheep."

The boy went to the pasture where the
sheep were nibbling the grass.

He walked up to a kind old mother
sheep and said, "Thank you, woolly
sheep; thank you for my nice new
coat. It is so good and warm."
The sheep said, "Oh, don't thank me; I
only gave my wool.
Thank God who made my wool grow."

The boy looked right up to heaven.
He said, "Thank you, God. Thank you
for my nice new coat."

26

ONE STARRY NIGHT

And there were shepherds in the same
    country abiding in the field, and
    keeping watch by night over their
    flock.
And an angel of the Lord stood by them,
    and the glory of the Lord shone
    round about them: and they were
    sore afraid.
And the angel said unto them,
    "Be not afraid; for behold, I bring
    you good tidings of great joy
    which shall be to all the people:
For there is born to you this day in
    the city of David a Savior, who is
    Christ the Lord.

And this is the sign unto you: Ye shall
    find a babe wrapped in swaddling
    clothes, and lying in a manger."
And suddenly there was with the angel
    a multitude of the heavenly host
    praising God, and saying, "Glory
    to God in the highest, and on earth
    peace, good will toward men."

WHY?

Why do bells for Christmas ring?
Why do little children sing?
Once a lovely, shining star,
Seen by shepherds from afar,
Gently moved until its light
Made a manger cradle bright.

There a darling baby lay,
Pillowed soft upon the hay;
And its mother sang and smiled,
"This is Christ, the holy Child."
Therefore, bells for Christmas ring;
Therefore, little children sing!

—Lydia A. Coonley Ward.

31

JESUS GROWING UP

Joseph was a carpenter in Nazareth, and
　　Jesus liked to watch him as he
　　worked.

Sometimes He worked with the tools.

Sometimes He watched the birds as they
　　flew about.

Many times He walked in fields and saw
    the wonderful wild flowers.
There were violets, daisies, lilies and
    many other flowers there.
He called them "lilies of the field."
Jesus grew up in that beautiful place
    among beautiful things.
Soon you will read many stories about
    His busy life. They are all Wonder
    Stories.

LUKE 2: 41-52

And his parents went every year to Jerusalem at the feast of the passover.

And when he was twelve years old, they went up after the custom of the feast.

And when they had fulfilled the days, as they were returning, the boy Jesus tarried behind in Jerusalem; and his parents knew it not.

But supposing him to be in the company,
they went a day's journey; and
sought for him among their
kinsfolk and acquaintance:

And when they found him not, they
returned to Jerusalem, seeking
for him.

And it came to pass, after three days
they found him in the temple
sitting in the midst of the
teachers, both hearing them, and
asking them questions:

And all that heard him were amazed
at his understanding and his
answers.

And when they saw him, they were

astonished; and his mother said unto him, Son, why hast thou thus dealt with us? behold, thy father and I sought thee sorrowing.

And he said unto them, How is it that ye sought me? Knew ye not that I must be in my Father's house?

And they understood not the saying which he spake unto them.

And he went down with them, and came to Nazareth; and he was subject unto them: and his mother kept all these sayings in her heart.

And Jesus advanced in wisdom and stature; and in favor with God and men.

A BUSY DAY

Near the sea of Galilee is a city called
Capernaum.

Jesus lived in the city of Capernaum
much of the time.

Some of his best friends lived there.

When Jesus went away from the city
many people would follow Him.

Many days He was so busy that He
could hardly find time to eat or
sleep.

One day Jesus went out to a mountain.

He sat down on the mountain and talked
to the people for a long time.

When He came down from the mountain
great crowds followed Him.

39

In the crowd was a man who was sick.
Nobody could make him well.
The people did not want to get near the
    man, for they were afraid they
    would get sick.
The man looked at Jesus and said, "Lord,
    if you will, you can make me clean."
Jesus reached out His hand and touched
    the man, and said to him, "I will;
    be thou clean."
And the man was made strong and well.
Just then another man came to Jesus
    and said, "My servant is sick."
Jesus said, "I will come and heal him."
The man said, "Only say the word and
    my servant shall be healed."

Jesus was pleased because the man
believed that his servant would be
healed, and He said, "Go thy way."
When the man went home he found that
his servant was well.
Jesus had many friends in Capernaum.
One friend who lived there was Peter.
Peter had a good wife and her mother
lived with them.
She was a good old lady and helped her
daughter about the work.
One day the old lady became very sick;
she could not work any longer, and
she had to go to bed.
Her poor face and hands and body were
burning hot, and she was very sick.

After awhile Jesus and some of His
friends came to Peter's home.
Just as soon as they went in, some one
told Him that the old lady who
lived there was sick with the fever.
Jesus went right into the room where
she was lying; He took her hand in
His just as though He meant to
speak to her.
Then something wonderful happened!
The fever left the old lady, and she got
out of bed and began to work.
She helped to get the supper ready for
Jesus and the others.
Do you think Peter and his family loved
Jesus for His kindness to them?

43

JESUS AND A BLIND MAN

Once there was a blind man.

He had always been blind.

He had never seen his mother's face.

He could only put his hands on her face
and feel all over it.

He could feel the warm sunshine, but he
could not see how beautiful it was.

He could hear the birds sing, but he
could not see them fly. And he
could not see their beautiful colors.

This blind man had to beg because there
was no work for him in the city
where he lived.

There was nobody that could make his
eyes get any better.

He knew that he could never see.

One day something wonderful happened
to this man.

Jesus happened to be in the city where
the man lived; and as He passed
by He saw the man.

Some of Jesus' best friends were with
Him that day, and they began to
talk about the blind man.

Jesus wanted His friends to know about
God's power.

He wanted them to know that He was
doing God's work.

He went to the blind man and stooped
down and mixed a little clay.

Then He put the clay on the blind eyes.

He said to the man, "Go wash in the
pool of Siloam."
The blind man went to the pool, and
washed his eyes.
What do you think happened? His eyes
could see!

The man was very happy.

He went home to his father and mother.

They were so happy because their son
   could see.

Now he could see his mother's face!

Now he could see his father's face!

He could see the bright sunshine, the
   birds and the flowers.

He went about praising Jesus for
   making his blind eyes well.

BLIND BARTIMÆUS

Here is a story of another blind man.

This blind man's name was Bartimæus.

Bartimæus had been blind for many, many years.

He was a blind beggar.

He used to go out by the city gates on a very busy street and beg of those who went by.

One day somebody told Bartimæus about a blind man whom Jesus had cured.

Bartimæus wanted to know all about Jesus and the other blind man.

He wanted very much to ask Jesus to heal him.

Some one told him that Jesus had been in other cities and towns healing the sick, making the lame to walk and the blind to see.

Oh, how he wanted to see Jesus!

But he did not even dream that he would ever get near enough to Jesus to ask His help.

One day Bartimæus heard a tramp, tramp, as though a great crowd of people were marching.

At last he asked what the noise meant.

Some one said, "Jesus is passing by."

The poor blind man jumped up and started to the place from which the noise came.

He wanted to ask Jesus to help him.

He called out, "Jesus, son of David, have
mercy on me!"

The people told Bartimæus to be still.

But the man cried louder and louder.

He had heard so much about Jesus that
he knew the dear, kind Teacher
would make his eyes to see.

When he cried louder Jesus heard him.
He stood still and said, "Bring the
man to me."

When the blind man came up Jesus said,
"What do you want me to do for
you?"

The poor blind man was so glad to hear
Jesus' voice.

He said, "Lord, that I may receive my
sight."

The dear, good Jesus was never too tired
or too busy to help any one who
was in need, and you may be sure
that He helped Bartimæus.

Maybe you would like to know just
what Jesus said to the man. These
are His words: "Receive thy sight.
Thy faith hath made thee whole."

The most wonderful thing happened to
Bartimæus! He could see!

He was so happy that he told every one
what Jesus had done for him.

"All the people, when they saw it, gave
praise unto God."

54

A STORY IN VERSE

The blind man said,
>"Save, Jesus, I pray."
But the people said,
>"Stand out of the way."
The man cried louder,
>"Have mercy on me!
Open my eyes,
>That I may see!"

Then Jesus stopped
>By the blind man's side.
He touched the eyes,
>And they opened wide.
The man cried, "Praise God,
>For now I see!"
And he thanked the Teacher
>From Galilee.

ANOTHER STORY IN VERSE

And now by the shore
    Of Galilee,
The Master worked
    All quietly:
Made the blind to see,
      And the lame to walk;
The deaf to hear,
      And the dumb to talk.

The leper was cured,
    The sick made well;
All the works that He did,
    No one can tell.
He fed the hungry,
    The weak made strong,
And many a sorrow
    He changed to a song.

JESUS HELPING A DEAF MAN

One day when Jesus was near the sea of
    Galilee, some people came to Him
    bringing a man who could not talk.
The man could not hear either.
His friends came to Jesus and begged
    Him to heal the man.
They said, "Jesus, this man can not hear;
    he can not talk. Won't you heal
    him?"
Jesus was always glad for a chance to
    help any one.
He took the man away from the crowd.
He touched the man's ears and his
    tongue.

Then Jesus looked up into heaven, and
    said, "Be opened."
The most wonderful thing happened!
The man's ears were opened, and his
    tongue was loosed, so that he could
    speak plainly.
And the man was glad.
He went about singing God's praise.

A POOR, WITHERED HAND

Jesus was walking with some of His very dearest friends one day.

It was the day on which all the people went to church, so Jesus and the men went into the church together.

There He saw a man who had a poor, weak hand.

This man's hand was all withered.

He could not work with it.

It was just a wee little hand, perhaps no bigger than yours, and it was all wrinkled.

Many times the man had tried to use it, but he could not.

Jesus was always anxious to help any one, and when He saw the man He felt very sorry for him.

He knew just how any one who could not use his hand must feel.

He said to the man, "Rise up."

The man stood up and Jesus said to him, "Stretch forth thy hand."

The man did as Jesus told him and his hand was made well.

Now he could use it! Now he could work!

How he thanked Jesus for curing him!

Every time he looked at his hand he said, "How thankful I am! I will always work for Jesus."

A THANKFUL MAN

One time Jesus had a long trip to make.
He was going to the city of Jerusalem.
He was going along the road and came
to a little town.
Just at the edge of the town there were
ten men standing.
They were standing away from the
other people.
When any one came near these men,
they would hold up their hands
and say, "Unclean! Unclean!"
That meant that the men were sick and
nobody must come near them.
The men had a dreadful disease called
leprosy.

No doctor could cure them.

The men felt very sad. Nobody could
touch them.

They could not go home to their families.

The men had heard about Jesus.

They had heard that He could cure all
kinds of sickness.

They had heard that He could give blind
people their sight.

They had heard that many lame people
had come to Jesus, and that He
had made them strong and well.

When they saw Jesus coming, they began to cry to Him, "Jesus, Master,
have mercy upon us."

Jesus knew what was the matter with
them.

His great, kind heart was full of pity
for the men.

Jesus never passed by any one who
needed His help.

He knew these men needed it now, and
He was glad to help them.

He turned to them and told them to go
on their way and show themselves
to the officer of the church.
The men turned to go, and as they
started the most wonderful thing
that you can think of happened!
The leprosy left them, and they became
strong and well.
There was one man that went back to
thank Jesus for what He had done.
He threw himself down at Jesus' feet
and thanked Him over and over.
The other nine men went on their way
and did not even thank the kind,
loving Master for what He had
done for them.

Jesus was so glad that one man had
come back.

He must have felt sorry that the others
did not, for He said, "Were there
not ten? Where are the nine?"

Then Jesus said to the man, "Arise, and
go thy way; thy faith hath made
thee whole."

It must have been a great surprise to
the friends of this man when he
went home.

All the friends who loved him were
happy and glad. They were not
afraid to touch him now, because
he was well.

The man never forgot to thank Jesus.

293

70

HELPING A SICK MAN

Once there was a poor sick man.

He had been sick for many years.

The Bible tells us that he had not been
able to walk for thirty-eight years.

You can not even think how long that is,
but it is a long, long time.

This poor man had heard that there was
a pool of water at Jerusalem.

The pool was called Bethesda, and every
year the sick people would go up
to the pool of Bethesda, hoping
that they might be cured.

There were great crowds around this
pool sometimes.

There was a certain time of the year
when an angel would go down into
the pool and the waters would be
troubled.

After that, the first one to get into the
water would be cured of any
disease he had.

Many people lay near the pool, waiting
for the waters to be troubled.

These sick people knew that just as
soon as the waters were calm and
still again, some one would be
cured, and each one hoped to get
in the water first.

This poor man that had been sick so
long was there.

He had been there many, many times before, and every time when he thought he might get into the pool, some one else stepped in before him.

He lay near the pool, hoping and praying that somebody would help him.

He was lying on a mat which he used all the time for a bed.

One day as he lay there something very wonderful happened.

Somebody who was very kind, Somebody who had cured very many sick people, came along.

It was Jesus, on His way to Jerusalem to the great feast.

He stopped to speak to the man.

Jesus knew how long he had been there
and how long he had been sick.

He looked at the man very kindly and
said to him:

"Would you like to be made well?"

Here are Jesus' own words:

"Wilt thou be made whole?"

And the man said to Him, "Oh, sir, I
would like to be, but there is no
one to help me.

When the water is troubled, before I
can get into the pool, somebody
else gets in before me.

If I could only get into the pool, but
there is no use trying!"

75

Jesus was so sorry for the poor man.

He did not say, "I will stay and help you get into the pool when the water is troubled."

He just said to him, "Arise, take up thy bed, and walk."

And the man was made well. He arose and took up his bed and walked.

He must have been very happy.

How good it seemed to be walking along like other people!

Do you not think that the dear ones at home must have been very happy when they saw him coming home?

Do you think they all thanked Jesus?

JESUS HELPING ANOTHER MAN

Once there was a very sick man.

He had a dreadful disease called the
palsy.

The man could not hold his hands still,
they just shook all the time.

He could not walk because his poor old
body shook so hard.

No doctor could make him well.

So many people tried to help him, but
they could not.

His friends did not think that he would
ever get any better.

They said, "He will just have to lie in
bed; he will never walk again; he
will never be able to feed himself."

But one day some good news came.
Some one said, "Jesus is here again."
When the man's friends heard that Jesus
    was in their city, they said, "Let us
    try to take the man to Jesus."

The man was so glad when his friends told him about Jesus, and he was willing to do anything that would make him better.

The man was lying on a mattress; that was his kind of a bed.

He said to his friends, "How can I ever get to Jesus?

"I can not stand or walk, and He is so busy that I can not ask Him to come here."

The friends said to this man, "We will carry you. We will take you right to the house where Jesus is."

The men were very careful as they took hold of the corners of the mattress.

They did not want to hurt the poor man
in any way.

Out from the house they started, down
the street to the home where Jesus
was talking to the people.

There was a great crowd of people at
the house where Jesus was.

They were crowded just as close to Him
as they could be.

There was no more room in the house,
not even about the door.

When the men reached the house, they
were sorry to find such a big crowd,
for they could not get inside.

They thought of the little stairway on
the outside of the house.

They said, "Let us carry him up the stairway; then we can lift some pieces of the roof and put the bed down through that."

And that is just what they did.

They carried him very carefully up the stairway, then they laid the mattress down on the flat roof.

They lifted some of the tile from the roof and let the bed down near the place where Jesus was standing.

Jesus saw that the men all believed that He could help the poor sick man, and He was pleased.

He said to the sick man, "Arise, take up thy bed and walk."

Then a wonderful thing happened!
The sick man got up and walked, and
   everybody in the house saw him.
The man picked up his bed and took it
   home.
He was so happy that he praised Jesus
   all the time.
Do you suppose his friends were happy
   too?

O COME, let us sing unto the Lord: let us make a joyful noise to the rock of our salvation.

Let us come before his presence with thanksgiving, and make a joyful noise unto him with psalms.

For the Lord is a great God, and a great King above all gods.

In his hand are the deep places of the earth: the strength of the hills is his also.

The sea is his, and he made it: and his hands formed the dry land.

O come, let us worship and bow down: let us kneel before the Lord our maker.

For he is our God; and we are the people of his pasture, and the sheep of his hand.

—Ps. 95: 1-7.

I WILL lift up mine eyes unto the hills,
from whence cometh my help.

My help cometh from the Lord, which
made heaven and earth.

He will not suffer thy foot to be moved:
he that keepeth thee will not
slumber.

Behold, he that keepeth Israel shall neither slumber nor sleep.

The Lord is thy keeper: the Lord is thy
shade upon thy right hand.

The sun shall not smite thee by day, nor
the moon by night.

The Lord shall preserve thee from all
evil: he shall preserve thy soul.

The Lord shall preserve thy going out
and thy coming in from this time
forth, and even for evermore.

—Psalm 121.

85

Hofmann

A BIG STORM

In the country where Jesus lived, there
is a beautiful sea called the sea of
Galilee.
Jesus liked to walk along the shore of
the sea of Galilee.
Sometimes friends were with Him.
Many times He went to the shore alone.
One day He had been busy making the
sick people well.
He had been telling the people stories
and talking about God's work.
He had worked all day long and in the
evening He was very tired.
He was so tired that He felt He could
not work any longer.

Often when Jesus was tired He liked to
go out on the sea in a little boat,
so that He could rest.

This time He said to His friends, "Let
us go across to the other side."

And they started out.

Jesus was so tired that He sat down in
the end of the boat and went to
sleep.

Soon a great storm came up.

The wind blew and the waves dashed
high.

The waves dashed higher and higher,
until they came over the edge of
the boat.

Jesus was still asleep.

91

The friends that were with Him were
very much frightened.
Sometimes these friends that were with
Jesus called Him, "Teacher."
They loved Him very dearly and they
did not see how He could sleep in
that hard storm.
They were so afraid, that at last
they awakened Him.
They said, "Teacher, don't you care if
we are all killed?"
Jesus awakened and saw how badly
frightened His friends were.
He spoke to the sea and the stormwind.
This is what He said to them:
"Peace, be still."

Then a wonderful thing happened!

The wind stopped blowing and the
waves went back, and in a minute
everything was quiet.

Jesus' friends had never seen anything
like this happen before.

Then they began to see that there was
nothing in the world that He
could not do.

He could make the sick people well.

He could make the blind eyes to see.

He could make the lame legs to walk.

He could make the deaf ears to hear.

And He could speak to the great storm
and say, "Peace, be still," and it
would mind Him.

A LITTLE LUNCH BASKET

Not far from the beautiful sea of Galilee
lived a little boy and his mother.
The boy had heard some people talking
about Jesus.
He had heard them say that Jesus had
made many sick people well.

He wanted to see the man who could
cure the sick, and make the blind
eyes open.

One day the little boy said to his mother,
"Mother, will you let me go to hear
the great Teacher today?"

She said, "Yes, if you will be very
careful."

He said, "Oh, Mother, I will be careful."

The mother thought he might stay all
day, so she fixed a lunch for him.
You will think it was a very little lunch,
but it was all the boy needed.
The mother took five small barley cakes
and two dried fish, and fixed them
in a little basket.
When it was ready the boy started over
toward the shore where the crowds
always went to see Jesus.
He was very happy as he went along.
He did not stop to listen to the bird's
song; he did not stop to play, but
hurried on as fast as he could.
At last he found himself in a big crowd.
He saw a mother take her crippled child
to Jesus, and he saw the child walk!

He saw many sick people trying to get
near enough to speak to Jesus.

And at last he saw Jesus with some of
His very dearest friends get into
a boat and go out on the sea.

He wondered where they were going.

Then he heard some one say, "Oh, He is
going across to the other side.
Let us go, too."

He saw a great crowd of people start.

Some of them were running, others were
walking, and he went with them.

It did not take very long to go around
the upper end of the sea, and soon
they were all on the other side.

When the people looked and saw Jesus
coming, they were all glad.

Jesus felt so sorry for the people, that
He went right to work healing all
those who were sick.

After a while Jesus' helpers went to
Him, and told Him that it was getting late.

They told Him to send the people away
to get something to eat.

Jesus had something beautiful planned.

But He did not tell His friends what
He was going to do.

He just said to them,

"You give them something to eat."

His friends began to look around.

One friend, whose name was Andrew,
came back and said to Jesus,

"There is a little lad here that has five
barley loaves and two fishes."

Jesus said, "Bring them to me."

Andrew asked the boy for his lunch.

The boy went with Andrew and gladly
gave his lunch to Jesus.
The boy did not know the wonderful
thing that was going to happen.
Jesus asked His friends to tell the
people to sit down on the grass.
He told them to sit down in groups of
fifty and one hundred.
Then Jesus took the loaves and fishes and
looked up to heaven and thanked
God for all His good gifts.
He blessed the loaves and broke them.
His friends began passing the loaves
and fishes out to the great crowd.
Nobody had ever seen such a wonderful
thing happen before.

As Jesus broke the loaves there were
more and more!

And as the friends passed the lunch
to the crowd there was more and
more of it!

Every one in all that great crowd had
all he could eat, and there was
so much left over.

Jesus said, "Gather up all the pieces
that nothing be lost."

And the friends gathered up twelve
baskets full of pieces.

How happy the boy must have been!

The mother, too, was very happy when
he reached home and told her that
he had given his lunch to Jesus.

102

WHAT CAN I DO?

I can not help like the laddie,
    With loaves and fishes, I know;
But I can feed the little birds,
    Out in the cold and the snow.

JESUS BLESSING THE CHILDREN

And they brought young children to
him, that he should touch them:
and his disciples rebuked those
that brought them.

But when Jesus saw it, he was much dis-
pleased, and said unto them, Suffer the little children to come unto
me, and forbid them not: for of
such is the kingdom of God.

Verily I say unto you, Whosoever shall
not receive the kingdom of God as
a little child, he shall not enter
therein.

And he took them up in his arms, put his
hands upon them, and blessed
them. —Mark 10: 13-16.

104

JESUS GOING HOME

Jesus was getting ready to go away.

He was going back to His Father in
heaven.

He knew that His friends could not go
with Him.

But He wanted them to know how
beautiful it is in His heaven home.

He wanted them all to come and live
there forever with Him.

One evening He had a long talk with
them.

Jesus' friends loved Him and they did
not like to have Him go away.

He told them not to be sorry.

Here are His own words:

"Let not your heart be troubled:
    believe in God, believe also in me.
In my Father's house are many
    mansions; if it were not so,
    I would have told you; for I go to
    prepare a place for you.
And if I go and prepare a place for
    you, I come again, and will receive
    you unto myself; that where I am,
    there ye may be also.
And whither I go, ye know the way."

Jesus had been very kind and good.

He had healed many sick people.

He was always doing good wherever
He went.

But there were some people who did
not like Jesus.

They were always trying to hurt Him.

At last they took Him and put Him on
the cross.

Jesus' friends were there, but they
could not help Him.

He was on the cross until He died.

Then He was put in a tomb and some
soldiers were put there to watch.

The wicked people said, "Maybe His
friends will take Him away."

While the soldiers were watching a
bright light shone.

The light was so bright that the soldiers
fell down just like they were dead.

Then something very beautiful
happened!

Jesus came out of the tomb!

He had risen from the dead!

It was just daylight on Sunday morning
when the two Marys went to the
tomb.

They went to take sweet perfumes.

When they reached the tomb an angel
was sitting inside.

He saw that the women were afraid and
he spoke to them.

175

111

He said, "Do not be afraid. I know ye seek for Jesus, but He is not here. He is risen! Come, see the place where the Lord lay."

The women were very happy. They turned to go away and met Jesus. They were very glad.

Jesus told them to go and tell His friends that He was living.

Many times He talked to them.

At last one day He went out with some of them to a hillside.

He gave them some beautiful messages.

Then He lifted up His hands and was carried right up to heaven.

And there He is to-day watching over all His little children.

FORGET NOT

My son, forget not my law;
But let thy heart keep my command-
      ments:
For length of days, and years of life,
And peace, will they add to thee.
Let not kindness and truth forsake thee:
Bind them about thy neck;
Write them upon the tablet of thy heart:
So shalt thou find favor and good under-
      standing
In the sight of God and man.
Trust in Jehovah with all thy heart,
And lean not upon thine own under-
      standing:
In all thy ways acknowledge him,
And he will direct thy paths.
Be not wise in thine own eyes;
Fear Jehovah, and depart from evil.

—Prov. 3: 1-7.

"I would be true,
  For there are those who love
    me."

A BEAUTIFUL COAT

In the long-ago time there was a man
whose name was Jacob.

Jacob was a very rich man.

He had lots of cattle and sheep and
camels.

Jacob had twelve sons, and they helped
to take care of his cattle and sheep.

Some of these sons were grown up.

There was one who was just a boy.

His name was Joseph.

Jacob loved Joseph very dearly.

Joseph was the youngest of all the boys
who watched Jacob's flocks.

Maybe that was the reason Jacob loved
him so dearly.

The boys were very unkind to Joseph
  because their father loved him.
One day Jacob gave Joseph a new coat.
It had many pretty colors in it.
Joseph was very happy when his father
  gave him the beautiful coat.
Jacob was very happy too.

225

It made the brothers crosser than ever
to see Joseph's new coat.
They were so ugly and cross that they
would hardly speak to him.
One day Joseph's brothers had to take
the flocks a long way from home.
After they had been gone for some time,
Jacob called Joseph and asked him
to go and find his brothers.
He said, "I would like to hear from them."
Joseph started out to find his brothers.
He came to a place where he thought
they would be and hunted around,
but he could not find them.
A man saw Joseph wandering around
and asked what he was hunting.

Joseph said, "I am hunting my brothers.
    Do you know where they have
    taken the flocks?"
The man said, "Yes, I heard them say
    they were going to Dothan where
    the pasture is better."
Then the man showed Joseph the way.
Joseph went on and on, and at last he
    saw his brothers with the sheep.
The brothers saw Joseph, too, and they
    began to say bad things about him.
They planned to do him a great wrong.
Some of the brothers wanted to kill him.
But there was one brother who stood
    by Joseph.
He said, "No, let us not take his life."

This brother was Reuben.

Reuben tried to think of some way to help Joseph.

He said, "Let us put him in that pit away out in the field."

Reuben thought if they would put Joseph in the pit that he would watch his chance to help Joseph out and take him back home.

When Joseph came up he tried to tell them what his father had said, but they were unkind to him. They took his beautiful coat from him and put him into the pit.

After awhile some travelers came along the road.

The brothers knew that these travelers
   were going to a far country.
They said to each other, "Let us sell
   Joseph as a slave.
That will be a good way to get rid of him.
They called the travelers and sold
   Joseph as a slave.
Reuben was away out in the field.
After awhile he came back to the pit to
   help Joseph out.
But Joseph was not there!
Reuben felt very sad.
He did not know what to do.
The brothers took Joseph's beautiful
   coat and dipped it in the blood of
   a goat.

Then they carried it to their father.

They said, "We have found this.

Is it Joseph's coat?"

The poor old father said, "Yes, it is my son's coat."

The old father did not know that Joseph was living and that he was going very far away from home.

It was not very long before Joseph reached the new country.

The men who had bought him sold him as a slave.

They sold him to the captain of the king's soldiers.

One day somebody told a bad lie about Joseph and he was put into prison.

115

He was such a good prisoner!
Everybody liked him.
Sometimes the prisoners had dreams.
Joseph told them what their dreams
meant.
One day the king had a dream.
He sent for Joseph to come and tell him
what his dream meant.
God gave Joseph the power to tell the
king the meaning of his dream.
The king was so pleased with Joseph
that he took him out of prison.
He said, "You are the wisest man in my
kingdom."
Then he gave Joseph beautiful clothes
and put a gold chain about his neck.

He said, "You shall be a ruler in my
country, and all men shall bow to
you."

After a long time Joseph's father and
his brothers and all their families
came to live in Joseph's new home.

His brothers were sorry that they had
treated him badly, but Joseph was
very good to them.

He forgave them for all the wrongs
they had done him.

Do you think Jacob was glad when he
found that Joseph was alive?

Do you think Joseph was glad when his
old father came to live in the new
country?

GOD SPEAKING TO A LITTLE BOY

One time there lived a good man and
woman.

The woman's name was Hannah.

They had no little children, and Hannah
was very much grieved about it.

She went to the temple and prayed that
God would send her a little boy.

By and by a little baby boy came to live
with Hannah, and when he was old
enough she took him up to God's
house and left him there.

She said to the good man who had
charge of the temple, "God gave
me this little boy, and now I am
going to give him to God's work."

257

131

132

Then Hannah prayed to God and went
away.
This little boy's name was Samuel.
Every year Samuel's mother made him
a new coat and took it to him.
She was very happy when she was
making the new coat for him.
Samuel helped Eli, the good man in the
house of God, for many years.
Eli taught him about God's work, and
showed him how to do everything.
Samuel pleased God by doing right.
One night, after Eli had gone to bed,
Samuel lay in his little room.
The voice of God called, "Samuel."
The little boy answered, "Here am I."

He ran into Eli's room and said, "Here
am I; for thou calledst me."
Eli said, "I called not; lie down again."
God's voice called a second time.
Again Samuel went to Eli and said,
"Here am I; for thou calledst me."
But Eli said, "I called not, my son; lie
down again," and Samuel obeyed.

135

A third time the voice called, "Samuel." And a third time Samuel went to Eli and said, "Here am I; for thou calledst me."

Eli saw that God had called the child. He said to him, "Go lie down, and if He call thee, say, 'Speak, Lord, for thy servant heareth.'"

Samuel went and lay down in his place.

God came and stood and called again, "Samuel, Samuel."

Samuel answered, "Speak, Lord, for thy servant heareth."

God gave Samuel a great message.

When the morning came Samuel told Eli all that God had said to him.

Then Eli knew that it was really God who had talked to Samuel.

Samuel grew and grew and God was with him all the time.

Everybody in all the country around knew that he was to be one of God's helpers and they all loved Samuel.

A LITTLE CAKE OF BREAD

Many years before Jesus came to the
earth there lived a good man
whose name was Elijah.

One day Elijah went over to a city.

He was very hungry.

He had not had very much to eat for
a good while.

When he came to the city gate he met
a woman who was gathering sticks.

Elijah asked the woman for a drink of
water.

When she started for the water, he
called to her and said, "Will you
bring me a little bread too?"

The woman said to him, "I have only a little meal and a little oil. I am gathering some sticks so that I may cook it for myself and my son. After that is gone, we will die, for we have nothing more."

Elijah said, "Fear not; go and make the bread, but bring me some of it first. After that you may make for yourself and son."

Then Elijah told the woman that God had sent her a message.

He said to her, "The jar of meal shall not waste, neither shall the cruse of oil fail, until the day that God sends rain upon the earth."

That was God's way of telling her that
  she should not want for anything
  to eat; that she should have plenty
  for herself and her son.
Every day the woman gave Elijah some
  food.
Every day she made a cake for him.
When she looked into the jar of meal it
  was just as full as it had been.
When she looked into the cruse of oil
  there was just as much as there
  had been before.
The poor woman helped Elijah so much!
One day Elijah helped her.
Her little boy was sick.
He was so sick that he died.

The poor woman turned to Elijah in her sorrow.

He said, "Give me thy son!"

Elijah took the little boy in his arms and carried him upstairs into his room.

Then Elijah prayed to God that the little boy might live.

He said, "O Jehovah, my God, I pray thee, let this child's soul come into him again."

And the little boy lived!

Then Elijah took him downstairs and said to his mother, "See, thy son liveth!"

The woman said to Elijah, "Now I know thou art a man of God."